Corinne's Fin

Dayle Dabney
illustrated by Ashley Teets

Be happy from
for Jew!
Dayle Dabney

Headline Kids
an imprint of Headline Books, Inc.
Terra Alta, WV

Corinne's Fin

by Dayle Dabney

illustrated by Ashley Teets

copyright ©2016 Dayle Dabney

To order additional copies of this book or for book publishing information, or to contact the author:

Headline Kids
P. O. Box 52
Terra Alta, WV 26764

Tel: 800-570-5951
Email: mybook@headlinebooks.com
www.headlinebooks.com

Published by Headline Books
Headline Kids is an imprint of Headline Books

ISBN-13: 978-1-882658-68-8   Hard Cover
ISBN-13: 978-1-882658-64-0   Paperback

Library of Congress Control Number: 2016939639

Dabney, Dayle
Corinne's fin
   p. cm.
    ISBN 9781882658688
    ISBN 9781882658640
 1. Children's 2. Fish 3. Special Needs
Dabney, Dale Fiction

This book is dedicated to my three daughters:
Erin, Shannon, and Meghan who have taught me
many of life's lessons throughout the years.

Corinne could swim from shore to shore,
dawn to dusk, and season to season.

Flowers hugged the
warm water of Lavender
Lake and filled the air with
sweet perfume.

5

Her underwater bulletin board was filled with first place blue ribbons. Corinne won EVERY goldfish race at Lavender Lake; every summer, every fall, every winter, and every spring.

Baby fish would come and say, "Corinne, please show us all your pretty Oranda goldfish ribbons again! We want to win some racing ribbons one day!" They couldn't help but stare at her fire-engine red lips.

Her strength was
deep within her
magnificent flowing
fins. They could swish
extra water with each
swirling stroke across
the small lake from
start to finish.

Corinne practiced her swimming strokes every day in the middle of the shimmering water near the NO FISHING sign. NO FISHING signs also surrounded the edge of Lavender Lake amid the purple flowers. There were families having picnics every day around the circle of purple flowers—enjoying lavender sugar cookies for dessert.

Corinne was always the first place winner, even if the little boats were passing and the waves were rolling. Corinne could swim around and under the boats and still be the fastest swimmer. She felt like a true champion until the day of the terrible accident.

Corinne was practicing her swimming strokes in
the middle of Lavender Lake when she got caught on
something sharp and curvy. One of her special flowing fins
was trapped by a large treble fishing hook! Three hooks in
one! Someone was fishing from one of the boats.

Fishing was not allowed so Corinne forgot to be careful.
She expected everyone to follow the NO FISHING signs.

Corinne pulled and tugged to get free, but her striped flowing fin was trapped by that shiny metal fishing hook.

"Oh, no! What shall I do?" Corinne wailed with fright as her red head trembled. She jerked so hard and so many times to get free, she tore off the bottom half of her right flowing fin.

It floated away like a toy sailboat as a small wave rippled by. Corinne was finally free but with only half a flowing fin. "Oh no! What happened? I lost half of one of my strong swimming fins!" sobbed Corinne.

Corinne cried and cried. Not only was her fin ripped, her heart was broken, her dreams were shattered. When Corinne tried to swim, she could only glide around in large circles. The half fin could not keep up with the other strong fin so around and around she would circle.

"Will I ever swim from edge to edge of Lavender Lake again?" Corinne was afraid of the answer to that question.

Her friends tried to comfort Corinne. Her friend, Bluebell, felt sorry for Corinne. She cried out loud whenever she tried to talk to Corinne.

"Oh, Corinne, why did this happen to YOU of all the swimming fish? You're the Champion!" bellowed Bluebell.

Bluebell could only see what Corinne had lost.

Her friend, Flame, was so mad about the three-way
fish hook that his scales would bristle and shiver.
"Why don't people follow the laws like they should?"
Flame was so angry he could not help Corinne.

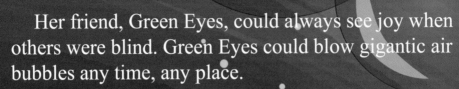

Her friend, Green Eyes, could always see joy when others were blind. Green Eyes could blow gigantic air bubbles any time, any place.

Green Eyes told Corinne he would visit her every day for a month. He would teach Corinne how to blow bubble blankets. Corinne, amid her tears, blew bubbles with Green Eyes.

The bubbles gathered together like frog eggs and formed a bubble blanket. Corinne rested under the bubble blanket for a while each day. New thoughts grew while she was under the crystal clear covers.

Corinne found a new Corinne. Her friend, Green Eyes, believed in Corinne and now Corinne believed in herself.

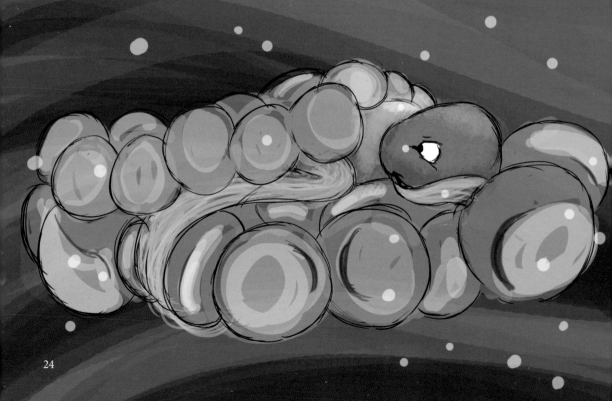

Corinne chose a new path. She encouraged the young fish to swim out far into the gentle rippling lake to see all the wonders and then come back near the edge and tell her of their magnificent adventures.

Corinne imagined she was swimming along with them through the warm ripples.

All the young fish gathered around Corinne to learn the secrets of swimming far and fast. They practiced every day to get ready for the goldfish races at Lavender Lake.

"Please, Coach Corinne, teach us all that you know," they pleaded. And so she did.

"Ready, swimmers? Swish, Swish! Right, Left! Swish, Swish! Faster, Faster! Swish, Swish!"

Corinne loved to listen and coach the young fish before and after a day of strong swimming. She wrote about their adventures as if they were her own.

The young fish loved to visit her waterproof library and read her stories especially *Water Secrets, Frannie's First Win,* and *Champion Forever.* Corinne was so busy coaching and writing she had no reason to cry about her missing half fin anymore.

Corinne was ready to watch others swim the races at Lavender Lake every summer, fall, winter, and spring.

Corinne was FREE, free to be her new self from fin to fin.

Lavender Lake Cookies

½ cup shortening
½ cup butter
1 cup sugar
2 eggs
1 teaspoon vanilla extract
½ teaspoon almond extract
2 ¼ cups flour
4 teaspoons dried lavender flowers
1 teaspoon baking powder
½ teaspoon salt

Step 1   Combine the shortening, butter and sugar until light and fluffy. Beat in extracts. Combine the flour, lavender, baking powder and salt. Mix well.

Step 2   With two teaspoons, drop rounded mounds of batter two inches apart onto baking sheets.

Step 3   Bake at 375 degrees for 8-10 minutes until golden brown. Sprinkle with sugar.

Step 4   ENJOY Corinne's Lavender Cookies with milk while reading or listening to the story. Courage from Corinne will be coming your way.

Goldfish Anatomy

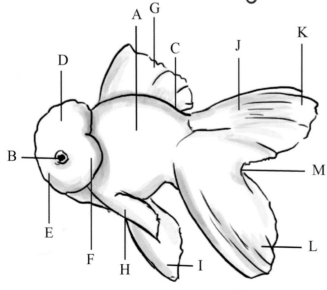

- **A-** Body
- **B-** Eyes
- **C-** Caudal Peduncle
- **D-** Cranial Region (of head)
- **E-** Sub Orbital Region (of head)
- **F-** Operculum
- **G-** Dorsal Fin
- **H-** Pectoral Fins
- **I-** Pelvic or Ventral Fins
- **J-** Caudal Fins
- **K-** Upper Caudal Lobe
- **L-** Lower Caudal Lobe
- **M-** Fork